SIX KINDS
OF LOVE

SIX KINDS
OF LOVE

SHEILA THOMAS

Illustrations by Grace Hanrahan

Matador
9 Priory Business Park,
Wistow Road, Kibworth Beauchamp,
Leicestershire. LE8 0RX
Tel: 0116 279 2299
Email: books@troubador.co.uk
Web: www.troubador.co.uk/matador
Twitter: @matadorbooks

ISBN 978 1800462 564

British Library Cataloguing in Publication Data.
A catalogue record for this book is available from the British Library.

Printed and bound in Great Britain by 4edge Limited
Typeset in 11pt Baskerville by Troubador Publishing Ltd, Leicester, UK

Matador is an imprint of Troubador Publishing Ltd

For Nigel

CONTENTS

INTRODUCTION

Six kinds of love

It is a frightening thought that, in modern 21st century society, we have more words to describe different types of coffee than we have to describe the most important thing in human existence: love. Not only is there just a single word in English, but I find it an especially useless one, as it cannot possibly convey the great range of emotions we use it to describe. The Ancient Greeks had a much wider range of words at their disposal to communicate what we recognise today as different kinds of love:

The six main types were:

Storge – The kind of love which parents and children can have and involves caring and commitment.

Eros – Romantic love involving attraction and intimacy.

Mania – Obsessive love which often involves unhealthy attachment and can lead to controlling behaviour.

Pragma – Practical love in which two people make a commitment to each other but do not share intimacy or passion.

Ludus – Infatuation which involves passion and desire but no commitment.

Agape - Universal love for mankind as a whole. Unselfish concern for the wellbeing of others.

The different types can, of course merge into each so, for example a couple who have been together a long time may have started out feeling great amounts of Eros which, over the years, develops into Storge or Pragma.

The characters in this collection of monologues would all say they act as they do out of "love". As one couple famously replied when asked if they loved each other, "Of course. Whatever love means". Perhaps the characters you are about to meet may help you to understand the meanings of love a little better.

STORGE

*unconditional love, such as the
love of a parent for a child*

SONNY BOY

SCENE 1:

A. is a late middle-aged woman, neatly dressed, permed hair, glasses. A suburban living room, with a sideboard in the background and a floral standard lamp is turned on. A. is seated in an armchair next to a side table with an old fashioned phone on it. Morning.

I was just getting ready to pop down to the shops when the phone rang. I only needed a fresh loaf, and an egg custard for our elevenses but I generally pop next door to see if Jean wants anything. She does the same for me when she's going down and she's saved my bacon no end of times when we've run out of something or other, generally bacon ...

Anyway, the phone rings and it's Robert on the other end asking if I could possibly go over to look after the kiddies, only Lynn's not well, but she has to go into work and he's got a full day of teaching followed by a meeting at the cricket club and then straight to Parents' Evening. Me and his Dad are so proud of him; he could easily have ended up in the

3

steelworks like his Dad and he would probably have gone in for football given half a chance, but I wasn't having any of that and made sure he got a proper university education, so he wouldn't have to work twelve hour night shifts like his Dad.

[Pause]

We were that proud when he came out wearing his cap and gown. His grandma started crying and I had a little cry too, 'cos none of our family had ever got above polishing cutlery or pouring steel. He looked a real picture.

[Short pause]

Anyway, he says, "Can you be on the one o'clock train? I can't pick you up but you know your way don't you? You can always get a taxi and then Lynn can get to her staff meeting at 4 o'clock." Well, I am always pleased to be needed and I didn't like to think of them kiddies being poorly and not having anybody there to look after them. So I said, "Course I can. Just let me take me curlers out and I'll be straight on the next 48 into town. Your Dad will just have to make do with the leftovers from last night's meat and potato pie for his tea". He quite likes that actually, says it always tasted better the next day. So I didn't see any problem and anyway them kiddies have to come first. It meant I would miss my chiropody appointment with Mrs. Wright but what the heck, I've walked about with these feet for years so a few more days wouldn't hurt. He says, "Don't forget your train pass, so you'll only pay half fare." As if I would. That train pass has been a godsend to me. I can travel all over with these half-price fares since I retired. Jean says, "I'm hardly ever at home." "Bill forgets what you look like," she says, but it's not true; I just like to get out and about, see what's going on in the world. Robert always pays my train fares when I go over to see them. He's good like that; that's how we brought him up.

[Pause]

So, I managed to catch the one o'clock to Barnetby and, as I'm getting out of the taxi, I see Lynn coming out of the house, with a nice three quarter length coat on and her hair done up. "I've left a note with what to do," she says. "Damian's just thrown up and Suzanne's been in the toilet for the past half-hour. There's a bucket under the sink and some antiseptic wipes in the cupboard. Shan't be long. It's just a meeting and then some of the staff are going for a drink afterwards."

[A. smiles, smugly]

Well, I am not easily fazed. Having brought up a child in the middle of the Blitz and got him through measles, German measles, chicken pox and rheumatic fever, I am no stranger to the sick bowl or the toilet bowl for that matter. So I went in, rolled my sleeves up and set to work ...

SCENE 2:

A suburban kitchen. A. has just finished a cup of tea in a
china cup. She is still in her outdoor coat, scarf and is in
the middle of taking her gloves off. Late morning.

Well, I was gasping for a cup of tea when we got back. Suzanne's birthday party really took it out of me and Bill is worn out, so he's having a nod in the chair after his tea. He could sleep on a perch could Bill; mind you, I could have as well today. And it was bitter cold on that train. You'd think with all this investment in the railways that they talk about they'd be able to afford some heating in the carriages, let alone a buffet car so we could have some hot tea, but no, it was not to be on the 5.30 from Barnetby. We all just had to snuggle up and huddle up as best we could to keep warm – it reminded me of the war! Anyhow, we were pleased to celebrate Suzanne's birthday with her, though we didn't seem to see much of her and she spent most of the afternoon in the backroom with her friends from school. Still, she seemed to like the new "Swatch Watch" we bought her for her birthday present. In fact, she seemed to be using it all the time while we were there. Whenever I saw her she had her face glued to it and she seemed so taken up with it, I could hardly get her to say two words to me and her grandad. It must be because it's new.

Robert and Lynn just had a party at their house, as they said what's the point in going to the expense of hiring anywhere? They said they wanted to keep things nice and homely, so they set out a few sandwiches and crisps on the kitchen side and kept the tea and coffee flowing. They'd invited a few guests round too, so it was quite a gathering … I spotted their old neighbours, Maria and Howard standing by the Aga, keeping warm no doubt, so I made a beeline for them. She's always been quite chatty whenever she's seen me hanging out washing for Lynn and she complimented me once on the whiteness of the children's nappies. You can't hope to get them white without a 'boil wash' I told her, but she said she thought an economy wash was good enough for nappies and so did Lynn. They don't seem to take a pride in things like we used to. Anyway, I know she's been having a few problems with her elderly parents so I asked her how they were. "Well I'm not sure," she said. "The last time I spoke to them, they were packing their suitcases for a Caribbean cruise, so I suppose they're probably limbo-dancing to some Bob Marley by now." "Oh, that's nice for them," I said. "I didn't know they were interested in ballroom dancing." "They've decided to live in the moment," she said, which is another way of saying "we've decided to spend your inheritance." "Well, you can't blame them for wanting to enjoy themselves," I said, although I was actually thinking I can never understand parents who want to do that. Why do people have children if they just want to put themselves first all the time? I don't see the point.

By this time, Bill was looking lost, no sign of Robert and Lynn was busy chatting to Lesley who she works with and is an aspiring Headteacher. "Does anybody know the cricket score?" he asked. They must all have been deaf because he had to ask again, "Has anybody heard the latest cricket score?" I thought Robert's cricket club were at the party; Howard Buntingford,

John Moore, Johnny Simpson and Ted Rowley, but none of them seemed to hear Bill asking about it, so in the end I took him into the living room and we sat down and put the telly on to find out. England only needed 86 to win, so he was pleased. I went and fetched us some tea and everybody seemed to be having a nice time talking to each other, so me and Bill just sat and watched the cricket. It seemed a shame when we had to go to get the train as England only needed 12 runs by then, but there was only one bus an hour with it being a Sunday and we mustn't miss that 5.30 train. We didn't want to trouble Robert and Lynn when they were having such a nice time with their friends.

SCENE 3:

A. is sitting in an armchair in her bedroom. Next to her is a neatly made bed with a floral bedspread. Early afternoon

I've never been so worried in my life before. He's never done anything like this before you see … gone missing. And there was nothing to let on that he was going to go missing. He just came downstairs as usual and sat down with the paper and a cup of tea for an hour like he does, while I got the washing on and then, just as I was hanging out that new brushed cotton nightie that I got from Marks; he comes up and says "I'm just going to see Frank Bullivant."

"Frank Bullivant?" I said.

"Yes, you know Frank," he said.

"I don't," I said.

"You do," he said.

"I don't," I said, "Who is he?"

"I know him from work, don't I? Anyway, I've got to go and see him," he said.

Well, he'd already got his fleecy jacket and his cap on and he was bent down tying up his shoelaces when I said,

"Where does he live, this Frank Bullivant?"

"I know where he lives," he said.

"Well, where then?" I said.

And by that time, he had tied his shoelaces and was off down the path and through the gate. He left it open, like he does, as if he couldn't get to this Frank Bullivant quick enough. I don't think he'd even combed his hair he was in such a rush to get out, but I don't suppose it will matter if he bumps into anybody we know, as you can't really tell under his cap.

Well, that was the last I saw of him for the next few hours. When it got to 8 o'clock I started to think "He's late, he must be having a right old chat with Frank Bullivant", but when it got to 9 o'clock and he still wasn't back, I started to get on edge, so I did a couple of rows of knit 1, purl 1 on Damian's new jumper I'm knitting for him to try and steady my nerves, but it didn't do much good. So, I went round to Jean next door who gave me a cup of tea and a Rich Tea to try and settle me down, but she's a woman of action is Jean, so she gets straight on the phone to Robert and gets him to come. I couldn't really tell what she was saying to him as their phone is in the hallway next to the mirror and umbrella stand, but she seemed to be on quite a while with him and I could hear her keep saying, "Robert, your Dad's gone missing." I don't know if it was a bad line, but she seemed to have to repeat it a few times to get him to hear. She came back in and she says, "Well, he's coming and he says he can be here in an hour once his cricket club meeting has finished."

"That's good of him," I said.

Jean didn't say anything.

[Short pause]

Well, time goes on and there's still no sign of Bill, so Jean goes out in her Honda Civic to see if she can see him, but comes back and says we should ring the police if he doesn't turn up soon. "Oh, he'll probably be on his way back from Frank Bullivant's by now and he'll have missed the bus, knowing him" I said.

And then, lo and behold who do we see strolling down the road without a care in the world, but Bill. "Where the devil have you been?" I said and it sounded cross, but it came out all wrong because I was actually that pleased to see him.

"I've been to see Frank Bullivant, but he must have moved, 'cos there was someone else living where I thought he lived," he said.

"Well, where have you been then?" I said.

"I don't know," he said.

[Pause]

By this time, Jean had made a cup of tea for us both and Bill drank his as though he'd pinched it and asked if he could have some whisky in his next cup. "You've had us all worried sick," Jean said and she sounded angry, but I know she was as pleased as I was to see him.

There's a knock at Jean's door and guess who it is? Robert has managed to get over and he comes in to Jean's living room, as our house was in darkness. He's the only person who doesn't look very pleased; it must have been the long drive. Jean said, "Oh, you're here then! We wondered if we were going to find your Dad lying dead somewhere when he went missing. They need looking after, what with all this upset." "Oh well, my Dad's turned up now, so there's no need for me to stay is there?" Robert said. Jean didn't say anything.

"Well, if you need to get back, love ..." I said. Bill was still drinking his tea with whisky in it and didn't seem to be listening. "At least have a cup of tea with them and they could do with somebody with them tonight. They've had a hell of an upset" Jean said. "Well, I'll just have a quick cup" said Robert, "I don't want to be too late back."

Jean slammed the cup of tea down so hard I thought it was going to go through her lovely glass topped mahogany occasional table. And he drank it quick and drove off, so me and Bill went back to settle down for the night. We hadn't been up that late for ages. As we are getting ready for bed, Bill says,

"Was that our Robert I saw in Jean's front room just now?"

"Course it was, I said, "Don't you know your own son?"

"I just wondered if I'd imagined it," he said, "cos I don't remember seeing him there for very long."

"No, he wasn't there very long," I said, "He's got to get back."

SCENE 4:

A. is in a hospital café. An empty cup of tea in a paper cup is on a plastic table by the side of her. She is sitting on a hard chair. Late afternoon.

He's asleep now. Thank goodness. I never want to live through another day like that again. It started out alright this morning. We'd had our breakfast, two Weetabix and a cup of tea, and Bill had just settled down for his usual read of the paper and was just making his third cup of tea when he suddenly says,

"I feel rotten."

"What sort of rotten?" I say.

"I don't know; I just don't feel right" he says, and he stops making his tea and I notice he's left his last one which is most unusual for him.

"Well, have a lie down and see if you feel any better," I say.

"That's not going to do much good, the way I feel," he says.

"Well, we'd better get you to the doctor then," I say, and I get on the phone to Dr. Leddy's surgery but there's no appointments till a week on Thursday.

"He'll have got better by then!" I joke, but actually it's no laughing matter, cos Bill is lying on the settee holding his belly and looking grey.

I don't know what to do, 'cos they tell you not to go to A&E unless it's a proper emergency but I think this actually is. So I get a taxi to take us and, lo and behold, when they see him at the hospital, he's put right to the front of the queue. So we didn't have to wait, but I'm not sure that's a good thing in this situation. Anyway, they take him in and say he's got 'pancreatitis' whatever that is and he's to be kept in.

I rang Robert when I got back from the hospital to tell him, only I got Lynn instead who said she'd tell Robert when he got back, but it sounded like she'd tell him that his magazine subscription had arrived. "He's got pancreatitis, or at least that's what I think they said" I tell her. "Well, Robert will try and get over sometime, bye" she says and cuts me off short. "Sometime soon, I hope," I thought to myself. It would really perk him up to see Robert again. He was the apple of our eye, that lad. Such a sweet child and clever too. All we ever wanted, with his ruffled hair and scuffed knees from playing football. We thought we were the luckiest people alive when we had him.

Anyway, I've not heard from him yet. He's probably had a busy day. But he should have got the message from Lynn by now … . Perhaps he'll come over tomorrow. It would be nice to have somebody with me … … .

SCENE 5:

A. is standing looking out of the window, neatly dressed in black, in a small kitchen holding a cup of tea in a china cup. A funeral Order of Service is on the table with a photo of an elderly man on the front. Early evening sun is coming gently through the window.

It all went very nicely. I think he would have been very pleased with the turnout. Of course, there's always some who can't make it for one reason or another. Carol had a very bad cold apparently and would have come but she had to steam her sinuses according to Richard and he showed up with Peter looking as though the pair of them had had a few Jack Daniels before they came. Then there was Adrian and Marion who could only spare an hour or so as they had to get back to look after Marion's mother who has had an incident with a burst pipe in her bathroom. They can only ever spare an hour, except when they're on a cruise, when I imagine they have all the time in the world to spend on the sun deck. He seems to work in just single hours does Adrian, like when he used to visit his mother in his lunch hour so he wouldn't need to take up any of his weekend … always just the hour.

[Short pause]

Still, the vicar did a lovely service. He didn't know Bill of course. They never do, do they these days unless you're in church on a Sunday, which Bill never was. Just weddings, christenings and funerals, but he said his prayers every night and that counts for a lot more in my book. He gave me a Bible when we got married and I've kept it in the top drawer of my bedside table ever since. I've never been a big churchgoer myself, but I never miss 'Songs of Praise' on a Sunday. That's how we were. Just trying to live a decent life. The vicar mentioned his love of sport which more often than not amounted to watching the horseracing on the telly on a Saturday afternoon and doing the football pools on a Friday night, but I do remember him playing football with Robert in the yard for hours on end when he was a little lad and the pair of them used to play tennis in the park on Sunday teatimes when he was a bit older. "You need to throw your ball a bit higher," he would say. We did laugh. And then Robert would cry because he'd lost and his Dad would pull him up sharp and say, "Well, you'll win next time if you throw your ball higher when you serve," and he'd soon be laughing again.

The vicar made light of the time Bill had TB but I wish he hadn't. I thought I'd won the pools when he came out of hospital, 'cos lots of them didn't. When I had TB, the girl next to me died in the night and I thought I was going to be next. Even when you get over it, people know you've had it and they're not the same with you somehow. But Bill said it didn't matter and we were both the same anyway, so why didn't we go to the pictures and watch the new Cary Grant. I'm so pleased I did. Just look at what we would have missed if I hadn't. There would have been no Robert.

We chose some lovely music for him as well. I couldn't stop crying when I heard Bill's favourite, Al Jolson's 'Sonny Boy', but I managed to get myself together for 'Abide With Me', although I thought the rest of them could have put a bit more effort in, and I sang it as well as I could, for Bill . I don't suppose Bill could hear us, but you never know do you?

[Long Pause]

He made it to the funeral with Lynn and the kiddies, just in time. He's so busy with work these days, but anyhow he made it. I thought he could have worn a tie but I suppose they're all 'down with the kids' these days in schools. Anyhow, he was there on the front row with me and he seemed quite moved, even giving me a tissue when mine had run out. He gave me a lift too after the reception. They'd put on a lovely spread, plenty of ham and cheese sandwiches, some 'exotic' salad that seemed to have little seeds in it which turned out to be quinoa, some 'Beres' pork pies and I had asked especially for Bill's favourite – quiche and I had four slices of that. I couldn't really stay to enjoy the trifle and chocolate cake afterwards as Robert and Lynn wanted to get off to the council offices and I needed to go with them. In fact, I was the main person who needed to be there, according to Lynn. Apparently, there were some documents they wanted me to sign, to do with buying our house. I always thought it was rented from the council but

Robert says no, these days it's better to buy and he knows a lot more about it than me. It was a shame I had to dash off, as I'd made up a photo album to show everybody all the happy times in Bill's life. There's one of him when he was a young lad playing with his brother and sister, the day he started in the steelworks, our wedding photo and me with no flowers cause it was wartime and Robert's first baby photos with his Dad and his graduation with us all looking so proud.

Still, things have to move on ... I'll have to make my own cups of tea from now on ...

She hums 'Sonny Boy' as the light fades.

PRAGMA:

Practical love

CHEERFUL CHARLIE

SCENE 1:

G. is seated on a kitchen chair Next to him is a vase of roses.
A door is open looking out onto a garden

Well, I'm worn out. I've been at it since 10 o'clock this morning. The garden looks a picture now, though. I'm particularly pleased with how I've done the lawn edges. They look as though I measured them with a ruler. I didn't, but it's not a bad idea. The hyacinths I planted out are just showing through and there's already a carpet of snowdrops underneath the apple tree. It looks like a work of art, especially now I've pruned back all the roses. The Ena Harkness is doing well now after a bit of a difficult start and it looks lovely next to the Boule de Neige.

I cut some of the Cheerful Charlie to bring in the house for Mother. We bought that rose just after my Father died. She said it would remind her of Charlie's smile. I always take special care with that rose. It's been going a long time now, 35 years, and it still gives us some lovely blooms every year. 'It's like your father smiling at us every year,' Mother says. I try to smile as much as I can, be a "ray of sunshine" for her. We're very happy actually, looking after the garden, walking down to the shops, reading the paper. I take her for the odd drive out on a Sunday afternoon in Father's old Merc. We don't go too far though; we don't want to put too much mileage on her, the car, not Mother of course, but we go for a cup of tea and sometimes we might even go to Staveley Hall for a light lunch. She likes looking round the picture gallery there. She must have seen all the pictures dozens of times, but I never mention that. I think she finds it comforting to go to the places she used to go with Father. When I tell the neighbour where we've been, she says, 'Why don't you branch out a bit? You could have a run to the coast, or go up to London for the day on a supersaver ticket.' But we don't want to branch out. I was chatting to her just now, as I was doing the pruning and she says, 'My niece is coming to visit this afternoon. Do you want to pop round when she's here? I think you'd get on very well.' This is her idea of saying that, at my age, I should have a girlfriend. Well, what she doesn't realise is that I **have** had a girlfriend, but it's never worked out and I don't want one now anyway, what with looking after Mother so she's barking up the wrong tree with that one. 'Oh, I've got a lot of baking to do this afternoon' I said, which was true as I wanted to use up the last bit of buttermilk for some nice fruit scones. Mother likes those, especially, but they've got to be made with buttermilk, not ordinary milk. 'Your Father always said he could taste the difference and so can I', she says, and she is right, they are better with buttermilk. You can't always get it but Mother and I have found an "artisan" cheese shop that does a range of dairy products and so we go there on a Thursday now. That gives us Fridays to go to Mr. Atkins' butchers and get the meat for the Sunday roast. His shop's been there years and it's the son serving in there now, but Mr. Atkins is sometimes there still and comes to ask Mother how she is. 'He gets to look more and more like Charlie, doesn't he?' Mr. Atkins says. 'Do you think so?' says Mother. I don't know what they mean. I can't see it myself.

SCENE 2:

G. is seated looking out of the window onto the garden with a colour catalogue of country cottages for holiday rentals open on his lap. He is holding a mobile phone.

We've been thinking of having an adventure. Not a very big adventure obviously, but having a bit of excitement, you know. In fact, I'm feeling very pleased with myself. Well, we both are, Mother and me. Mother said she fancied a change of scenery, so at first, I suggested going up to London for the day but she said no, she wanted somewhere quiet but refined. She won't go abroad, not since the war. Says she's worried she won't be able to get back to England if something happens and to be honest, I'm not that bothered about looking at foreign countries. They don't always have our standards do they?

So, anyway, I popped in to the travel agents when I went down for the paper and they had this 'English Country Cottages' brochure which sounded just down our street. We had a lovely evening looking through it and we toyed with the South Downs and the Cotswolds but we settled on the Yorkshire Dales as Mother said she had some lovely holidays there with me and Father when I was a little lad. 'You were about 5 I think' she said 'It's difficult to remember though, as you always seemed old for your age.' Anyway, it should be lovely. We've managed to get exactly the same holiday cottage in Pickering that we had last year. We'll take our own bedlinen and pillows of course, as we don't want to be uncomfortable and I'll pack the travel kettle, because you can't always bank on there being tea and coffee making facilities in the room and even when there is, it's generally just a few cheap tea bags, instant coffee and some plastic milk. We were very early booking, probably the first ones, but you've got to be organized if you want to get ahead of the game, haven't you? It was a lovely cottage though … just enough kitchen cupboards for storage and a nice artificial log fire, not a dirty real one and the bedrooms were immaculate. Mother says, you can never be too careful. We take our own cups and saucers too, on that very principle. She can't be doing with those large mugs that everyone seems to prefer these days; honestly some of them are as big as buckets in these new coffee shops. We prefer a nice china cup on a nice china saucer. We generally pack the teapot too, seeing as we know just how long to warm it for. Father always used to have a Royal Doulton china cup. I can see him with Mother now, sitting together in stripy deckchairs on the lawn, next to the pompon dahlias having their cup of Assam. It's not a variety I particularly liked, but I seem to have got the taste for it now.

Well anyway, we're off to Pickering next summer and I will take the opportunity of going to visit my gentleman's outfitters, Mr. Braithwaite. He always likes it when Mother and I call on him because I think we must be his best customers. I stock up on everything when I am there – socks, sock garters, underpants, vests, shirts, braces, sleeve holders, ties, tiepins, collar stiffeners, casual corduroys, and I have been known to buy the odd tweed jacket from him, although he doesn't always have the ones with the reinforced elbows in stock.

Mr. Braithwaite has a nice spacious fitting room too, which we like. I always like to try everything on and it ends up a bit like a fashion show with me keep popping out to show Mother. Mr. Braithwaite sometimes makes Mother a cup of coffee we're there that long and she always says, 'Oh, you're spoiling me, Mr. Braithwaite.' He always replies, 'Well, you're worth spoiling, Mrs Clifford' which makes her blush and go all flustered.

The amount we spend at Mr. Braithwaite's probably **does** make it worth his while to spoil her with a cup of coffee, but I don't mind. 'You remind me of your Father when he was young' she said once when I tried on some burgundy slacks and a V-neck pullover, but I couldn't see it myself. He never wore burgundy slacks and he always wore round necks, but she **would** have it. Mr. Braithwaite joined in and said how burgundy was definitely my colour and the next thing I know Mother had decided I was buying them. I don't mind. When I stock up at Mr. Braithwaite's I don't need to buy any clothes for the rest of the year, so it's really a saving.

After Mr. Braithwaite's, we generally go for a cup of tea at the Copper Kettle. I have a custard tart and mother has an Eccles cake, except when she's feeling adventurous she'll go for a vanilla slice. I wish she wouldn't though, she always get halfway through one and then says, 'Do you want some of this?', which I never do but I always end up finishing it off because I don't like leaving anything when we've paid for it. They're always so messy, vanilla slices, too. You never know whether it's better to use a knife and fork or just go for broke and shove the whole lot in your mouth and wait for the custard oozing out onto jumper the minute you take your first bite. It's a dilemma, which is why I would never choose a vanilla slice in the first place. The custard tarts at the Copper Kettle are just right for me. Mother and I steer well clear of their scones though…you can tell they don't use buttermilk.

[Pause]

I've just phoned to reserve the cottage and I did have to laugh. The young girl who answered asked me the name of the guest who would be staying and of course I said 'Mr. & Mrs. Clifford. 'So one double for one week' she went on before I corrected her and asked for two singles. 'Oh, sorry, I thought you were a married couple', she apologised. 'Yes, lots of people think that' I said, though I don't know why, there's a 32-year age gap between us. Anyhow, the cottage looks just like home from home. I think we're going to have a very nice time … … .

SCENE 3:

G. is sitting by the phone in the living room, looking worried

I'm waiting for them to call back. The care agency that is. I've left a message telling them our particular needs. They are very particular needs too. Mother is a very particular person. We need someone special; someone who would be like a member of the family. After the stroke, she can't really say very much now, but I can tell what she wants. I can see in her face what she wants. She doesn't need to tell me.

She's not going to take very kindly to having someone else in the house. It's just been me and her for nearly 35 years. I must say, I'm not going to like it much myself. I like it just being us two. I can't keep on like this though. Caring for Mother is more than a full-time job now. I know she only wants me though. But, if I don't get some help soon, **I** might not be here much longer. People have been very kind, though. Cynthia from across the way calls in some mornings to see how Mother is and stays about half-an-hour and the WI sent some flowers but none of them are here at 10 o'clock at night when I'm trying to get her to bed, or at half-past 2 in the morning when she needs the toilet, are they? That's when I could really do with some help. I do my best for her, of course I do, but sometimes, I don't really feel like her son. Someone was talking the other day about the changing roles in families, as parents age. Thought for the Day on the radio I think it was and I thought how true it is. When we're children we never think we will really be parents do we?

And I never have been. Playing at mummies and daddies is nothing like the real thing … …

[The phone rings]. Oh, that will be the care agency now … …

SCENE 4:

G. is wearing an apron and dusting the Royal Doulton figures on the sideboard.
He then arranges a vase of Cheerful Charlie roses in a vase next to a framed photo of his mother.

She didn't last long after the stroke. We only had the carers in for two weeks and that was it. They were very nice and smiley and very caring towards Mother, but Mother never seemed to like them much. I suppose they could never be me. Well, she's gone now. She doesn't have to put up with them anymore. She's with Father now. I hope she is, at least, but none of us really know do we? I've a feeling they **are** together, though, deep down.

So that just leaves me now. [*Pause*] I'll be alright. [*Pause*] I have the garden and the dusting. I have a very full life. I'll be able to sort out that dahlia bed and get those roses pruned. I might even enter the 'Best Kept Garden' competition next summer, you never know. I'll be able to turn those drawers out in the sideboard and the cupboards too. You never know what I might find. I might go to a car boot sale with the stuff I will find in there.

I won't be short of things to do, oh no, I've got a lot of interests. I'll go up to Pickering on my own and call in to Mr. Braithwaite's. It will be just like old times when Mother and I used to go. Except it won't be, will it? When Father died, Mother always had me. [*Pause*] The problem is, I haven't got her now, have I?

Bach's "Air on a G string" softly fading away in the background.

LUDUS:

Playful, infatuated love

KEEP CALM & CARRY ON

SCENE 1:

M. is sitting at a table in a cafe
A few tasteful prints are on the wall
There is a floral tablecloth and an empty teacup on the table

I can't wait to tell her, Stella, I mean. She'll never believe it. Not at my age. I think she thinks I'm past it, ready for the old folk's home, over the hill. Well, anyway, she's in for a shock ... I've met a man! We generally just chit-chat about people we know and I tell her how much I've enjoyed the poetry reading I've been to and she tells me how hard it is looking after her mother, now that she's become bedbound, but I look forward to seeing her as it gets me out of the house and we end up talking about quite philosophical topics like 'Is it always wrong to be selfish?' and 'Does someone have to be sorry to be forgiven?' Quite the modern, free-thinking women we are and we both enjoy a bit of intellectual debate.

Anyhow, there's not going to be much of that today. I've got something much more important to talk about than trying to sort out the human condition in 15 minutes. It's Lawrence. I could talk about him for hours because, well, there are so many aspects to him. He's fantastic looking for a man of 65, very distinguished features and lovely grey, glossy hair, 'lustrous' I think you could describe it as, and such a smart dresser. When I first saw him he was wearing a lovely chunky knit pullover and some tailored shorts and I noticed be hadn't bothered with any socks, just some nice Russell & Bromley brogues. I've just been away for the first time in ages on a group excursion to Sicily. I didn't want to go, but Stella said it would be good to get away for a bit and broaden my horizons. She thought Sicily would be just right for me too as she knows how much I enjoy a nice lasagne. So, I thought in a group you're bound to find someone to make friends with and not be stuck on your own like Billy no-mates, like I usually am.

Anyway, the trip didn't start too well when none of us could get the hang of the seating plan on the coach which they changed every day to stop people hogging the best seats all the time, and I had just sat in what I thought was my place, halfway down on the left, nearest the window, when someone said, 'I remember sitting in front of you, yesterday, so that must mean I'm in here', and they slid into the window seat in front. 'Yes I think you did', I said though I couldn't really remember but I noticed he had a nice open-necked shirt and some maroon chinos and I remember thinking what a sensible choice for today, seeing as we were going up into the foothills of Etna. Just then Elsie and Roy show up and they seem to think they were sitting in front

34

of me yesterday, so they should be in front of me again today and start hovering next to where Lawrence has just sat down.

They weren't in front of me yesterday, they were behind me, but they're easily confused. I said, 'Oh, I don't remember now', but like the perfect gentleman he is, Lawrence gets out of his seat and flashing his lovely white teeth he says to me, 'Would this seat be free next to you?' Well, I didn't think it was, as I sat next to a retired mechanical engineer from Reading yesterday, but I thought he might have got mixed up as well and gone to sit elsewhere. 'Yes, I think it is', I said and moved my little tote bag on to my knee. Lawrence sat down and said, 'Would you like a Fisherman's Friend?' 'Sorry, come again?', I said, 'Oh yes', and then I realised what he meant. 'The old ones are always the best ones aren't they', he said and I just nodded as I was struggling to catch my breath. It turns out that he was on the trip on his own just like me and had lost his wife two years ago, but was making an effort to 'broaden his horizons'. 'Just like me', I thought.

It turned out that he loves poetry as much as I do and in fact, he has even written some that was read out at his local arts festival. I told him about the poems I had written and he seemed particularly taken up with the one about wildflower meadows, said I seemed quite the William Wordsworth but I'm not sure if he meant Elizabeth. I hardly noticed the Sicilian countryside rolling by outside and when we arrived at the foot of Etna, I was gagging for a cup of tea, having been talking so much, so I was delighted when he said 'Would you like to come and have a glass of wine with me in the café. I'm not in the mood for going up in a ski-lift today? Well, I don't normally drink, but all

of a sudden, the cup of tea didn't seem too appealing so I said,'
'That's very kind' and he helped me off the coach. 'I don't know
if it's being in Sicily, but I feel we have a real connection' he said
as he poured our second glass of Nero d'Avola, 'I haven't been
able to talk to anybody like this, not even my wife', he said. I
didn't know what to say but I knew what he meant. I couldn't
remember talking like this with a man for so long, I'd forgotten
what it was like; 'Me too' was all I could get out and he handed
me his card with his address and number on it saying, 'We need
to keep in touch. No, more than that, we need to be there for
each other'. 'We do', was all I could say, even though my heart
and my head were racing. I have honestly never felt like this
before, not even when I was young. I suddenly felt life open
up before me and instead of living a little life I was going to
be living a full life. A life of poetry and music and wine, and
it's going to start now. I won't be available to go for coffee with
Stella on Thursday morning anymore … … …

SCENE 2:

*M. is drying a couple of cups and putting them away in her kitchen.
There is an open bottle of whisky and two glasses on the table.*

Well, it couldn't have gone any better; it really couldn't have.
I know a poetry reading is not everyone's cup of tea but it's
certainly mine and Lawrence's. In fact, with my flair for poetry, I
might describe it as a lovely cup of lapsang souchong with a slice
of lemon served in a Royal Doulton Citrus Grove china cup.

[smiles smugly]

Looking back on it, I think this has been the happiest evening of my life. We'd turned up early to help with the teas and put the Family Assortment out. When I say we, I am alluding to myself and Lawrence, of course. He'd jumped at the idea of coming over to mine all the way from Aldershot and I was so surprised when he said he'd come to the poetry reading. I'd been a bit wary of mentioning it as you know how men can be about women writing poetry, but he said he'd be delighted to come and support me. 'I was named after D.H. so I was bound to like literature', he said. 'D.H. who?' I said. 'Lawrence' he said and I felt a fool for not twigging on to what he was saying. I'm really going to have to step up to the mark with Lawrence, I can see. He's so clever and sharp-witted, but nice with it.

I'm going to have to read a lot more widely than Danielle Steel if I'm going to keep up with him. So anyway, he arrives with his case late this afternoon and I was feeling so good about me and him that when I showed him to the bedroom, I deliberately chose the one with the double bed. He didn't say anything, he's such a gentleman. He must have presumed it was just for him, but **I** wanted to hedge my bets. Well, you never know how things are going to turn out do you? So, I left him to unpack while I got us a drink, not the usual cup of instant coffee I would be having at 4 o'clock on a wet Wednesday afternoon in November, but a nice glass of Nero d'Avola, if you please. Lawrence had brought it with him 'To remind us of Sicily' he said. 'So thoughtful' I said, and I meant it. I've never met a man like Lawrence before. I can feel the rest of my life opening up in front of me like one of those valleys we drove through on the coach. We seem to have a meeting of minds and we have so much in common ... poetry and a love of the Sicilian countryside ... . He really is a catch. I can't believe it at my age and it happened just like that. We didn't need any of these dating websites that everyone seems to go on these days ... just natural chemistry. There's nothing to it really, if it's meant to be. Que sera sera, my mother used to say.

So, we go down to the community centre after finishing our little aperitif and Mr. Wren is already there, putting out some chairs in a circle. Straightaway, Lawrence goes to help him which I thought was lovely. How many men would do that? 'Hello Mike' I said to Mr. Wren. 'I've bought someone along with me this month'. And I could see he was a bit surprised. I think he had me down as a no-hoper. 'Lawrence Hill', pleased to meet you', said Lawrence, and in just those few words you could hear how erudite he is. They shook hands and then Lawrence says, 'I'm Margaret's boyfriend'. And there it was, he'd actually said it. It felt as though he was talking about someone else but I know he meant me. I never thought I'd hear those words again in my lifetime, but there they were clear as a bell. I saw Mike looking at my new cardigan from Marks and the jazzy necklace I'd bought to go with it and you could tell he was stuck for something to say. 'Well, thank you for coming along tonight' he said and wandered off to put the tea urn on.

By this time Angela and John have turned up and you could see they wanted to know who Lawrence was as well. Angela couldn't stop her eyebrows from going up six inches when I introduced him as 'my boyfriend', but she said it was a pleasure to meet him and had he read her collection of poetry for Christmas, available on Amazon at £5.99?

The usual crowd turned up and we make a start with the notices and procedures in case of emergency, then we get down to business and I'm called up to read first. I'm sure I blushed beetroot red but Lawrence squeezed my hand just as I was getting the book out of my handbag and that put me on track again. So inspiring …

So I start with 'The Boat' … "Launching out on the pond, she set on her course …" [*Pause*] And then it absolutely flowed. I don't know what came over me but it was like a dream and I wasn't in the community centre anymore but somewhere far away where life was a pleasure. I was that little boat being launched and my course was going to be very different from now, heading towards a new horizon. The clapping brought me back to the community centre and I looked at Lawrence's face which beamed pride and encouragement to me. I am trying to hold onto that feeling forever, but I think it will be easy, as I will have Lawrence to give it to me from now on. Speaking of giving, I want to show him how grateful I am for everything he's done for me tonight. I'll just take him a little nightcap in the bedroom and see what happens …

SCENE 3:

M. is sitting in an armchair by the side
of a table with a mobile phone on it
Early evening

'Never mind' they say 'never mind', 'never mind what?' Well, I'm not supposed to mind, so I can't. I've just been speaking to Lawrence. It's not his fault though; it's that daughter of his. 'She has needs' he says, 'that he has to consider'. And I'm not saying he shouldn't. It's just that I was so looking forward to our weekend away in Canterbury. Haven't been away for ages, no-one to go with really. We'd been getting it all arranged; train from St. Pancras and a lovely hotel in the centre, not too far from the Cathedral and near some very select coffee shops.

I thought he was very keen on it and I think he still is … it's just her. She needs him to look after Rocco apparently on Saturday night. No-one else can do it apparently. More like she can't be bothered to fix anything up. Easier just to get her Dad to do it. And he is her Dad after all, so he's not really to blame. It's her; I think she doesn't want him to have a life of his own, make his own decisions, spend his money doing what he wants to. It's easier just to get him to do what she wants. She doesn't realise what we have together, how magical it is and how devoted we are to each other. We've been talking about marriage … at my age! Of course, I would give up my council house here and move down to Aldershot. It would mean leaving friends like Stella and Angela, but my life has moved on, new horizons and all that. His daughter will have to get used to the new arrangement, whether she wants to or not, it's happening! She can like it or lump it. When I'm down there we can both babysit Rocco; I don't mind helping out, building bridges with her. It's just that this weekend would have been so nice. I haven't been to Canterbury since I was 15 and went on a school trip … still I sometimes feel as though I am still 15 when I am with Lawrence. Never mind, as they say …

She looks vacantly out of the window as the light fades.

SCENE 4:

M. is sitting in a hallway on the stairs
A suitcase is next to her, packed but unopened
She is dressed in a coat and scarf

'Is it my fault?' I said. 'No, it's no-one's fault?' he said. Well he would, wouldn't he? If it's anyone's fault it's his daughter's. Her face was like thunder when I turned up and I thought I might have got a cup of tea when I walked in, but no. You could tell they'd had words. There was a tension hanging in the air like taut wire. Quite a poetic description that, but I wasn't in the mood for poetry. There's only so many situations that poetry can be of any help and this wasn't one of them. I go into their lounge and sit near the window in the single armchair, so as not to cause any more tension by actually sitting next to her Dad, God forbid, and then he says, 'I'll put the kettle on.' 'Can

I put my case in my room, Lawrence?' I asked but he didn't answer. I expect he couldn't hear me as he was in the kitchen and she came in, sat down on the settee and said nothing. He came back with the tea in a 'Keep Calm & Carry On' mug, an expression which I've never really liked and he says to her that she might want to go and see what Rocco is doing. So she goes to see to Rocco who, as far as I can see, seems to be asleep in the back room and doesn't need seeing to at all.

'I am so sorry, Margaret', he starts off. 'What for?' I asked. 'For what I'm about to say, Margaret', he goes on. 'Oh' I said and I felt the familiar feeling coming over me. 'It's no-one's fault' he said. 'What isn't?' I asked. For someone named after a giant of English Literature, he was being remarkably unclear. 'It's not how I wanted things to turn out, but things just happen, don't they', he went on, not making himself any clearer. 'What things?' I said. 'Things' he said. 'What are you talking about?' I asked, and he said 'Life'. 'Life' I said, thinking he was going off into one of his philosophical moments. 'Yes, well, the future'. 'The future' I said, wondering where this was going, when he suddenly said 'Yes, a future that we don't have.' 'What? Are you ill?' I asked, and I could feel myself getting that familiar panicky feeling inside, thinking of how difficult life might become but we would face it together. 'No, I just don't think we can be making any plans to get married.' 'What's brought this on?' I asked. 'I've been thinking a lot and I've got to put Janie and Rocco first' he said. 'But nobody's asking you not to consider them' I tried. 'Well, I have considered them and it's best if we are just friends' he went on. 'Friends?' I said, 'Or friends with benefits or just 'friends' do you mean? 'Well, you'll still be up in Cambridgeshire and I'll be down here, so it will be a long-distance friendship'. 'Long-distance friendship' I said. I couldn't stop repeating whatever he said, like some devoted parrot. 'Yes, we're both 'silver surfers'' so it should work OK and we can email each other with stuff about poetry can't we?'

Some choice poetry came into my head, but somehow I couldn't say anything at all, even though thoughts were racing round my brain. I just looked down and felt suddenly very foolish, like that silly 14 year old schoolgirl with a stupid crush on a boy. 'So I think it's best if you don't stay' he said very matter-of-factly and it made me think he'd had all this rehearsed. 'But what about our new life that was opening up for us both? Are we just going to go back to our narrow little lives as they were?' I asked him. 'Well, I think we just reached the end' he said, flatly. 'What of the chapter or the verse?' I said, but it wasn't the time for unfunny jokes. 'I'll see you back to the station' he said, and picked up my case in a rather too business-like manner. 'There's a train at half past' he said.

So here I am. Back in "Home Sweet Home". I'll just go and make a cup of tea seeing as how I haven't had one all day. It might help me sleep … . How can you Keep Calm & Carry On … ?

SCENE 5:

*M. is sitting up in a hospital bed and talking out of one
side of her mouth very slowly*

They'll be coming in a minute to bring the next round of tablets.
I'll be rattling soon [tries to laugh]. Oh my head… They're
very good here … . Nurse Taff's very kind and that other one
… oh what's she called … I'd write it down if I could, but this
arm won't move. I don't remember what happened but I know
Mr. Williamson from next door found me and rang for the
ambulance. They say I've had a stroke. Probably caused by stress
they said. Well, I'm retired, I don't have any stress … not really.

Anyway, this voluntary woman came to read to me today and
she started reading something out of a women's magazine like
'love is the strongest of all passions; it attacks the head, the
heart and the senses.' I don't know where that has come from
but I told her it certainly attacked me. I don't get many visitors;
Stella's been and Mr. Williamson, but nobody else.

It's a long way for whatsisname to come … [*Pause*] . It's funny,
I used to love writing poetry. I can't write my own name now.
They say it will get better in time, when things have healed.
Well, they might be able to get back the feeling in a hand, but
I'm not sure about the feelings inside here [*she gestures to her chest*].
I get so tired now. Trouble is, if I nod off I miss the tea round …
still, what do they say 'Keep Calm & Carry On.'

The light slowly fades.

AGAPE:

Selfless love for mankind

THE UNWANTED SHEPHERDESS

SCENE 1

The stage opens on a church altar in the late evening. B., the lady vicar, is putting the candles out with a snuffer, still dressed in her vestments.

It went well tonight, I thought. People generally seemed pleased with the service, at least they all smiled as I shook hands with them as they left. Mike generally gives me a friendly peck on the cheek and he did so tonight, so I could have said anything in the sermon and he would still be pleased with my efforts. But tonight, even Simon looked as though he had found the whole experience uplifting... so uplifting, I thought he was going to pull my arm out of its socket he shook my hand effusively. Rachel and Cynthia too seemed to be in good spirits by the time we sang 'Make me a Channel of Your Peace' and I could hear Margaret bellowing out her contralto harmonies, so I know she was enjoying it. It leaves me with a warm glow all over when they are in this mood. I feel as though I really am a shepherdess caring for her flock... perhaps not a very youthful

47

or attractive shepherdess, but one that wouldn't want any of them to be lost, or in pain or just finding the going tough. It's on evenings like this that I know they feel my love for them and I know they understand. [Pause] I would do anything for them. This must be how Jesus felt when he preached to the crowds and they heard his message. This is why I do this job. I wasn't always a vicar ... I started out in social work which I suppose is not that much different from looking after a parish. They're pretty similar, now I come to think of it, but when I decided to become a vicar it didn't really occur to me that I would be doing pretty much the same job, just with a few more hymns and candles.

I love people you see. All kinds of people and I would do anything for them. My mother used to say she never got to taste any of the baking I did at school, because I had given it all away, to the ragged-looking boys on the bus before I got it home. I suppose I'm still doing that now, really, giving everything I have to others. I'm not doing it to be liked, either, it's something I have to do. I can't be any other way. Of course, it's nice if people do like me back, everyone wants to be liked don't they? But, to be honest, I get that nice warm feeling from loving other people and that's enough for me. I can live on that.

SCENE 2:

B. is sitting at home in the vicarage with a cup of tea on the kitchen table. Her labrador is at her feet asleep. She is dressed in her dog collar, a comfy cardigan and some slacks,

Well, you can't expect everything to go alright can you? Especially not meetings of the Parochial Church Council and especially not on a wet Wednesday night in November, but we have to have them, even if it does mean massaging a few egos and turning a deaf ear to some of the more militant members of the P.C.C. I knew they didn't like me taking Alfie with me to start with. Bernard said something about dogs not being technically allowed in the vestry, but he said it under his breath and I wasn't really supposed to hear. What he doesn't know is that Alfie can't be left on his own, not after his previous owner left him in a locked house on his own to die, while she went on holiday to the Maldives. When I adopted him they said I should be aware of his separation anxiety which was caused by the trauma of having been found after 4 days on his own. Apparently the RSPCA had to break in when a neighbour heard Alfie barking and she realized he'd just been left. But, Bernard isn't interested in that. He's more interested in the amount that comes in through the offertory every Sunday and how much we have to give to the diocese, 'the parish share' as it's called. I sometimes get the impression that Bernard thinks he is still the 'Managing Director', somehow 'in charge' of us all. He can be very direct at times, like when he said that we might get more income from weddings if the choir would 'buck their ideas up'. He doesn't appreciate that we are lucky to have a choir at all, since out of the eight ladies who volunteer, Mrs. Bellamy and Miss Goodman have had hip replacements recently, Mrs. Reese has her elderly mother to think of, Miss Jones has got cataracts and is too frightened to have the operation, so can hardly see the music. Miss Jacobs joined the choir to help with her recovery from severe anxiety and sometimes can't make the practices, so that leaves three able-bodied and that includes the organist! Still, Bernard doesn't mean badly. I know he wants the best for the church and he is obviously a very able man. We are fortunate to have him in the village in many ways. It is good that we can forgive him his directness and practice our Christian virtues.

He wasn't very happy tonight, though. First there was Alfie who seemed to put him off and then there was a debate about where the Christmas collection should go to which seemed to upset him, even though he got his way in the end. Mr. Wainwright had suggested we hold collections for a charity for the homeless girls. After all, wasn't Jesus born into homelessness in a stable?

Bernard was then worried about getting some money in to replace the church hymn books in two years' time and setting up a reserve fund for it. 'I thought you might have shown a bit more support for the hymn book idea, vicar', he said to me as we were putting the chairs away. 'I do understand, Bernard', I said, 'but this is Christmas we're talking about, isn't it, let's worry about the new hymn books in the New Year. 'They'll have fallen apart by then', he said, 'things do get worn out, you know'. 'I know', I said, gently.

SCENE 3:

B. is moving some playdough and paint from a table in the church and folding up the newspaper on it. There is a cloth and a bottle of white spirit on the table. She looks weary.

'Messy church' we call this. And it can be very ... messy I mean. I've just spent half an hour getting some glue off Mr. Winterbottom's pew. I mean the one where he usually sits, right at the front, so he can hear. He wouldn't take it very well at all if he ended up with glue on his nice corduroys. Anyway, I've managed to get it all off now. No-one would know.

I thought it was a good idea to open up the church to the local children, seeing as we can't get the numbers to run a proper Sunday School now. I used to love Sunday School when I was little. There were even prizes for 'Scripture' as it was called then and all the children used to parade up to the park for the 'Whit Sing' as we knew it. All the local churches gathered together to sing hymns, just for the fun of it. I'm lucky if I can get one church to come together to sign hymns. We've got the regulars, of course, but this is why I thought inviting the children and their mums and dads in would be a good idea. Of course, there mustn't be too much 'church' involved or they wouldn't come. We generally set up some craft tables, painting and we've got a project going to build a model of the village using recycled card boxes and yoghurt pots. At the end, I finish off with a story from the parables and a children's hymn. All very light, it doesn't take longer than ten minutes. I didn't realise how difficult it would be to get the children away from the craft activities though. I tried gathering them up to come down to the front so we could do our story and hymn and I went up and asked a few of them to make their way down to the front steps. 'I'll be there in a minute', Jacob Weaver said and then Mrs. Weaver said, 'He's just got to finish off his replica of the almshouses in the model village. He'll be there soon. He's such a perfectionist.'

Well, we'd finished off the story and the hymn and Jacob was still working on the almshouses and then his mother got his coat and they shot out of the door, whilst Mrs. Weaver shouted to her friend, 'Sorry, got to go, it's Jacob's violin lesson in ten minutes!' She didn't seem to see the collection tray as she was rushing out either. It's only meant to cover the cost of the parents' tea and coffee and juice and biscuits for the children, but most weeks it doesn't even do that. Still, Jesus did say 'Suffer the little children to come unto me.' I don't suppose he realised how much suffering would be involved in running a 'Messy Church' session.

The parishioners don't like it. Of course, they don't tell me to my face, but when I ask for volunteers, people have always got something else to do. Funny, there's never any trouble getting volunteers for the cake stall or the open gardens' fundraisers. They don't like the thought of children running around the church, actually having fun. Cynthia once said to me, 'You know, it's really just cheap childminding, 'Messy Church', they'll come to that, but they won't come to actual church.' Well, so what if it is. At least some of the message will get through. It's not the children to blame, anyway is it? Didn't Jesus teach us to love one another? That's all I'm trying to do … Oh, just seen a bit of paint that needs wiping off.

She gets up with her cloth and the bottle of white spirit towards the table

SCENE 4:

B. is dressed in a nice print dress. She is wearing some jolly Christmas earrings and wearing a party hat.
She is tidying up the lounge of the vicarage. There are empty glasses and plates strewn around.

I love Christmas, don't you? I love these get-togethers too. It's always nice to show the members of the P.C.C. how much they are appreciated. We all like to feel loved, don't we? I think they liked the buffet I put on. Something for everyone, vegans, vegetarians, pescetarians, gluton-free, omnivores … there's so many people to think of these days, aren't there? They all tucked in anyway and they all seemed to partake freely of the wines on offer. I ended up mainly talking to Rachel in the kitchen about her sister who is struggling to manage her autistic son. Most of the menfolk seemed to gather themselves into a corner and talk about whatever men talk about. I went over to offer them a refill of wine and they asked if I found village life too quiet compared to my last church. I used to be in the East End of London, which was a real challenge, I don't mind telling you. I loved it in lots of ways but, as I said to the menfolk, I came here for a bit of peace and quiet and I'm hoping to enjoy it for a long time yet! They seemed a little disappointed that I hadn't said it was too quiet which I thought was a bit strange, but perhaps it was just me. Bernard said, 'Oh, Neville loved the quietness of village life." Ah, the sainted Neville, my predecessor, the man who could do no wrong, perfect in every way, according to Bernard. 'Yes, I do too,' I replied but I did wonder what had made him suddenly start mentioning Neville, unless they had heard from him in his new church. [*Pause*]. It's very hard living in the shadow of someone you have only ever heard of, isn't it? Someone who seems to have what you will never have, no matter how hard you try.[*Pause*] Someone who is a man.

SCENE 5:

B. is sitting at her kitchen table in an old blouse, trousers and a cardigan. She looks tired and drawn. She is holding a handkerchief.

Oh, I'll try and stop now. I won't cry anymore. I can't help it though. It's all so unnecessary. Why couldn't they come and talk to me, instead of complaining to the Bishop behind my back? Its hit me right here [*she clutches her chest*]. The Bishop didn't know where to look when he was talking to me, so he kept fiddling with his watch and pretending to tidy his fingernails. 'I know you have meant well' he said earnestly, 'but I can't ignore what people are saying.' 'Well they haven't said it to me', I came back to him, quickly. He could see he'd have to play things carefully. 'They don't like your overbearing attitude at P.C.C. meetings.

These are their words, not mine', he said, looking me in the eye for the first time since I came in. I thought he was going to follow up with "Don't shoot the messenger" as though he had nothing to do with what was happening. 'Apparently, you've been bringing your dog along, when the parish rules state clearly that animals are not allowed in the vestry. You've allowed the church building to be damaged by letting children run riot. You've not given church finances the proper importance they should have and have allowed funds to be misappropriated to outside charities.' 'Misappropriated!', I barked at him. 'Who has said that?' 'I'm afraid I'm not at liberty to name names', he went on. 'They don't like you putting the church on Facebook and Twittering either.' 'Tweeting' I corrected him. 'What's that?' he asked, frowning as though he were a character from a Dickensian novel. 'It's what you call using 'Twitter', a social media site, to give comments on what's happening in the world', I explained. I felt like a teacher talking to a child.

'So they don't like me making it easier for people to come and visit the church, know where we are, what we stand for then?' I challenged him. 'Would they rather have the parish like it was a century ago with the Reverend Honeyman riding his bike through the village and raising his hat saying, 'Good morning' to everyone?' 'Well, they don't like things too modern. You know that and I know that,' was all he could say. 'It's the first time I've ever had a letter from your P.C.C. complaining about the way the church is being run and I must say, it came as quite a surprise', he went on. 'You mean, there were never any complaints about Saint Neville', I said and it came out more spitefully than I intended it to. 'I have tried and tried to love these people, all of them. I have done my utmost, there is no more I can give to them. [*Pause*] I suppose there's no building bridges after this?' 'No', the Bishop said quietly. 'They've asked for a new vicar, actually.' 'Already?' I asked, flabbergasted. 'Well, they would like to see Neville back in his post and that would probably be best for everyone in these circumstances. Create a bit of stability.' 'I suppose it would' I said. I knew when I was beaten. 'And Neville is something I will never be.' 'Oh, what's that?' the Bishop asked, relieved by my easy agreement.

'A man,' I said.

MANIA:

obsessional love

THE SADNESS
OF SLEEPING BEAUTY

SCENE 1

J. is sitting in a comfy armchair.
Behind her is a neatly stacked bookshelf.

I never thought I would meet a man. I don't mean 'meet a man' as in buying a magazine from Mr. Singh, the newsagent, but 'meet a man' as in actually 'meet a man to go out with'. It wasn't such a ridiculous thought as you might think. My whole life up to the age of 23 was spent surrounded by females... Mummy of course, all my aunts who remained strangely unmarried, the teachers in primary school, the teachers at my girls' school, the dons at my girls' college at Oxford, Miss Pringle my piano teacher. Daddy was there, of course, in between his long business trips, but he seemed to not really be there even when he was there. I used to say as a joke to my friend, Josephine 'At the end of my obituary, it will say 'She never married.'

It didn't seem so far-fetched then. And we were certainly expecting to have an obituary written about me. I was what people call nowadays 'an overachiever'. I just did what people seemed to want me to do. I always did my homework beautifully, I practiced piano for hours on end, but there was nothing else to do really, being surrounded by all these females whose idea of excitement was finding a new colour of silk for their needlepoint embroidery. Well, it's all changed now. I've got a man in my life and he's perfect. I know people have said that before but in this case, it's true. [She smiles, broadly].

He's absolutely my exact type. We couldn't fit together any better. There are not many men who enjoy discussing the finer points of Hegelian philosophy, but Michael does. We talked about it for hours in fact, just on our first meeting. I couldn't believe it. I had been invited out for tea in the Orchard by my good friend Toni and we were just tucking into our scones and Earl Grey when two men came riding through on a tandem. 'Oh, Simon, what a surprise! I didn't know you came here', Toni said in between mouthfuls. 'Well, I don't normally, but Michael and I are just having some fresh air and this is one of the least crowded cycle paths round here', Simon replied, gathering his breath.

'Well, come and join us, I suggested, which was amazingly forward of me, compared to how I usually am. 'That would be lovely, I'm knackered' said Michael which sounded rather incongruous, considering he was dressed in the most immaculate and expensive-looking corduroys and striped shirt, clearly emanating good taste. 'I'll go and order some more tea and scones' Toni offered, so she left me with Simon and Michael to make conversation, a situation I usually dreaded. 'It's a lovely day for a cycle ride, isn't it?' I offered weakly as a starter. 'Yes, I just had to get out of my room for a bit. Hegel was driving me mad.' 'Who's that then?' I asked, naively. 'The father of German idealism' Michael said, without a hint of sarcasm. 'Oh, a politician then' I said. 'Philosopher' he corrected, helpfully. 'He's not everyone's philosophical cup of tea, but I like him', he went on. 'So what does he philosophise about, then?' I wondered. 'Are you interested?' he asked. 'I can talk about him for hours, so you'd better get ready' he joked. 'Yes, I only know the French philosophers really, from the literature I've read, but please enlighten me on the wonderful Hegel', I added, trying to let him know that I have got a brain and have read some serious stuff in my time, but I needn't have worried, he just spoke from the heart and you could see his passion for his subject radiating through. He didn't even mind when I asked what the difference was between 'immanence' and 'transcendence'. To tell you the truth, I wasn't really taking in all the finer points of his clarification and I wasn't that bothered anyway. I was concentrating on the way the sunshine picked out the auburn glints in his hair and the way he used his hands so expressively to communicate his point. I felt like I had never felt before. I never thought I was capable of feeling like that. I seemed to revert to being thirteen years old again inside. I didn't want it to end, so when Simon said 'Well, we'll leave you two lovely ladies to enjoy the rest of the afternoon', I said 'Oh, we don't have anything much to do, do we, Toni?' 'Well, I do, actually' she replied, unhelpfully. 'And I've got to finish my paper on voltammetry', said Simon, 'So we need to be on our way. Hold on Michael I'll give you a hand', and he gently brought the tandem over to him. 'We'll see you around then, girls' said Simon. 'Lovely talking Hegel with you!' quipped Michael as they cycled off. You would have never known that he was blind.

SCENE 2:

J. is sitting at her dressing table.
She is in her wedding dress and taking her hair down.
She has taken her glasses off and is cleaning off her eye make-up.

This is a day I never thought I would live through. Me! Married! Yes, I know what you're thinking. How can a great, fat, bookworm like me ever get married. Well, I used to think that too, but then I hadn't bargained on meeting Michael. We have a total and complete meeting of minds. It's not a relationship that's based on the physical, like so many of them seem to be nowadays. It just doesn't seem to matter with us. We are working on a totally different plane. Most people wouldn't understand. I'm not sure Mummy and Daddy understand. They didn't come today, even though we invited them. They said they "didn't want to be party to the biggest mistake of my life." I think being their daughter has actually been the biggest of my life so far. A whole new life is starting for me and for the first time, I have someone at my side who understands me. He loves me to play the piano for him and you can see from the expression on his face, I can communicate with him through music in ways that people will never manage with all the words in the dictionary. Mummy and Daddy can see the advantages for Michael in marrying someone like me because, though I say it myself, I am a very caring soul. I like to have someone to look after and I plan to give my everything to caring for Michael. His parents were there today and seemed overjoyed. 'We are so pleased that Michael has found someone like you', his father said. 'Well, I'm so happy to have found him', I replied and I meant it, too. I can't wait for my life to start. I feel a bit like Sleeping Beauty, waking up from a long sleep to start married life with her Prince Charming. When I was little, it was always my favourite fairy tale. I never thought it would be like my life.

SCENE 3:

J. is sitting by the kitchen table.
Bags of shopping all over the table.
A bag of sugar is on its own on the table waiting to be put away. J. is making herself a cup of tea.

I am gagging for a drink. It's knackering isn't it doing a big shop and then putting it all away? It's taken me three hours and I'm not finished yet. I need to call at the delicatessen on the High Street to get Michael's favourite pâté, but I'll do that later, once I've got all this stuff away and made dinner. It will be ready for me to come into later on and I won't have to start cooking later in the evening. Michael only likes to eat after 8.30. Says it helps him sleep. I find a heavy meal has the complete opposite effect on me, but we're all different, I suppose. I would like to get some gardening done today, as well, but I think that will have to wait until tomorrow.

I'll just see if he can come down and help me unload the heaviest bag from the car. It won't take a jiffy with two of us. Michael! Michael! [*No answer*]. He's probably got his earphones on listening to Radio 4 and so is incommunicado. It really is a godsend, Radio 4, to people who can't get out. Although, Michael can actually get out. He's done all his mobility training and he likes it when I drive him to places in the car. We're even on a waiting list for a guide dog. Michael's support worker thought it would increase his independence to have a dog and she may well be right. She's trying to encourage him to apply for a job. As Michael says though, as a Philosophy graduate, he is completely overqualified to be a switchboard operator and he's much more drawn towards doing a 5-year course which would train him to be a psychotherapist. I think he would make an excellent psychotherapist, having faced so many obstacles in his life. He really does know what it's like to face adversity. I wondered if he might go into academia like I've done. I know quite a few visually handicapped people who have found their niche in academic circles and he's more than capable of doing it intellectually, I mean. He's more capable than I am, if anything, on that level. That's sort of why I love him so much. I feel he's the guide and I follow along. So much intelligence and yet so held back by a disability that's not your fault. Life can be very bittersweet can't it? [*Picks up the bag of sugar*]

Michael! [*with a little more exasperation in her voice*]. Oh well, not to worry. It will do later. No, wait a minute, no it won't, it's all the frozen stuff. I'd better go and get it now. I don't want frozen lobster all over the boot of the car ...

SCENE 4:

J. is looking bleary eyed. She is still in her nightie and dressing gown. There is a big pile of letters on the floor next to her.

Sorry, I'm not really with it today. Don't know what's wrong with me. I just feel exhausted most of the time. Can't sleep either, even though I'm worn out. Stress doesn't help I suppose, does it? I used to be at my best when I was under a bit of pressure. Never missed a deadline yet. Mummy always said I was a grafter and she was right, I always graft as hard as I can to make things right. It seems to make people happy. This feels like a different sort of stress, though. I'm not even sure that's what this is, but my support worker, Angela, says I mustn't have it. 'It won't help you to get better', she said, before she tackled the mountain of washing up in the sink. I felt so ashamed when she walked in, she doesn't have to do it, it's not part of her duties, but she says 'You've been looking after other people, now I'm looking after you.' By people she means Michael. We live in separate houses now even though we are still married, for health reasons now, mine mainly. Michael's parents were not best pleased with the separation. It means they have to curtail their retirement travel plans to the Caribbean, South

America and Alaska this year and actually come and help their son. That's not going to go down well with them, but Michael will be pleased, he doesn't mind where the help comes from, as long as it comes. He could keep six P.A.s busy! I would still help him now if I could, but it's doctor's orders I'm afraid. He's so grateful for everything. He once said how he would never have been able to do his psychotherapy course, if it hadn't been for me working full-time and looking after the house. I used to quite like driving him up to London to his course and waiting in the coffee shop, getting my marking done, while he had his seminar. I remember how he used to want to get back home straightaway afterwards, so he wouldn't miss listening to 'The Archers' in his study. It was never the same in the car, he used to say. I couldn't do it now, drive to London. I couldn't drive anywhere in fact. It's a good job I've got things to keep me occupied. There's the piano, my embroidery which I love doing and then there's always the admin for Michael which never seems to end. Piles and piles of it. He always says he is going to ignore any correspondence from organisations that refuse to write to him in Braille. It's lucky he's got me to sort it out for him. In fact, I'd better get on with it now. That's a red gas bill I can see there …

SCENE 5:

J. is dressed smartly in a suit.
She has her hair up.
She is sitting at the kitchen table.

Gosh, I will be glad to get these shoes off [*taking her hair down*]. Oh, that's better. What an eye-opener, the court today. Michael and I are now divorced. There's a sentence I never thought I would say, but it's true. It felt like living through a dream, actually, while we were in there. We had a nice lady judge and Michel looked so smart in his bespoke suit and bowtie. At first, I thought it was a bit too jaunty, but it actually showed off his funny side. Michael was always funny, if exhausting. I can't say I'm not pleased though. Peace and quiet is what the doctor ordered for me and I'm not likely to get it if I were still married. I think things have been worked out fairly, considering. The judge gave Michael 90% of our house and me 10% since, as a blind person, Michael has no income of his own and still has three years to go to finish his psychotherapy course. Although, now I come to think of it, how will I ever get my 10% if Michael doesn't agree to sell the house? Still, I did hold on to my pension. Good thing too, as I'm not sure I'm in any state to go back to work. Michael will be able to build up his own pension when he becomes a psychotherapist won't he? Yes, it all seems pretty fair to me.

It's good to think I can put these past few years behind me and enjoy some relaxation now. There's only me to worry about now isn't there? I can please myself, do what I like, go where I like. I might even go to Provence for a long holiday. Yes, that's what I'd like to do. [*She closes her eyes for a moment*]. Although, wait a minute, if I go to Provence for six weeks, that's going to leave Michael high and dry isn't it? Gosh, I hadn't thought of that. We can't have that. In fact, I wonder how he is now after the hearing [*Pause*]. I'll just pop round to see him … and I can tell him how I'm getting on with his admin…

She puts her jacket back on hurriedly and leaves

EROS:

Romantic love

GREEN SHOOTS

SCENE 1:

K. is in his cellar.
There are empty crates of wine bottles all around him.
He sits on a foldup chair to one side

I'm not sure I'll ever get over the embarrassment. Having to
come back and admit defeat. Get any old job. Just to see us
through. I keep saying us ... I mean me. It's like when I make
a cup of tea. I still get two cups out. I only need one these
days. Since we came back from France. It was meant to be
us living the dream. A vineyard of our own in the glorious
French countryside. No more putting up with the lockjam
traffic on the M11, no more enduring the endless meetings
about sales targets, no more petty office politics, no more
queuing to park in Waitrose car park on a Saturday morning.
No more of Emily trying to work her way up the education
ladder to the dizzy heights of Deputy Head and eventually
Principal. No more of her doing a full day's work at school

and then an evening of marking or report writing. No more dealing with parents who say their children should get 'more than 100%'. No more of any of that ... just living a simple life, tending the vines, making our own wine, eating rustic French cuisine, cooked in our own wood oven. Sounds idyllic doesn't it? It was ... for a while. We were happy for about the first three months. I mean really, genuinely happy. We got up and went to bed with the sun. We lived close to nature, just like we always said we would. We made friends in the village. French friends, the sort you could rely on to help you out in an emergency. We went for dinner in their homes and invited them to ours. The local young lads loved the seasonal work we were able to provide for them, tying the vines and picking the grapes. We all celebrated together after our first harvest, with a great barbecue. Sylvain brought his guitar and we sat round the fire until early morning singing songs and thinking how lucky we all were.

The luck eventually ran out though. Emily and I did our research as thoroughly as we could before embarking on our great French adventure. After all, neither of us had any experience of wine, other than enjoying drinking it. No-one mentioned how hard it is to make any money from it; it doesn't take much to throw all your plans and dreams off course. Just a few storms that wreck most of your vines, after you've paid your workers to tie them. Just a slight dip in the price of table wine that wipes out the small profit that you hoped you might make. Nothing much, but it's enough. It doesn't take much to throw a relationship off course either. It's easy when everything is hunky dory. It's when it's not, that you find out where the cracks are. It's when the novelty wears off and all you have left is being with each other.

In our case, being with each other all day and all night. At least, when we were both doing proper jobs, we had someone to come home to, something to talk about, something to give to each other. We were only able to give each other more problems after a while, after the first heady weeks of excitement had worn off. Emily tried to find some work teaching English, to help our situation and it did a bit, but it was a bit like turning up in a hurricane disaster area with a dustpan and brush to help with the clean-up … too little, too late.

We used to make a thing of telling our married friends with children, that we didn't want children. We described it proudly as a positive choice. Not for us, the endless paying out for new shoes and after school activities. Not for us, the constant worrying about little Sebastian and Jocasta and whether they have chosen the right options for their GCSEs. No, our life was going to be full of fun projects, something we could build together, something we could be proud of. Well, neither of us is very proud of how things have turned out. Don't they say 'pride comes before a fall.' It certainly has for us. Emily tried to put a positive spin on it for our friends, when she sent out the change of address cards – 'it's better to have tried and failed than never to have tried at all.' I'm not so sure. Failure is not all it's cracked up to be. It's painful and destructive and its hurts like hell.

SCENE 2:

K. sits at a table, wine glass in hand.
An opened bottle of wine is on the table.

I've done it. I've told her I've had enough. She thought I meant enough of the relationship. She'd be even more upset if she knew I really meant enough of her. We've used each other up, worn each other out. We are both bored stiff. We know what we each think about every subject under the sun … there's just nothing new to find out about each other. Of course, coming back has been hard and it probably has everything to do with it, but it's a difficult adjustment to make from sales executive to taxi driver and from Head of Department to supply teacher. That was all we could get, though. You can't afford to be too choosy when you've lost all your savings in a business venture that has gone so badly wrong, you were lucky not to be declared bankrupt. I picked up a fare today, a young couple who used to live opposite us. I could see him, looking, thinking he sort of recognized me and then finally plucking up the courage to ask me straight out, 'Didn't I used to know you from Southfield Road. I think you lived near me and Jackie, didn't you? You went abroad, didn't you?' 'Yes, that's me. We decided to come back', I said in my best non-committal voice, but you could see he was dying to ask why. 'That'll be £16.50' I said quickly, to put a stop to any more questions. 'Oh, righto' he said and gave me the cash. 'Is this what my life is going to be from now on?' I thought, as I drove off. That one thought led onto other, more serious thoughts and by the time I'd got back to the taxi rank I'd convinced myself I had to do something to change, something radical, something big. The biggest part of my life has been spent with Emily; she knows me inside out ... that's the problem. Looking at her face, puffy and blotched with tears, her puzzled desperation, her pleading confusion after I told her tonight. I'm not sure she saw it as a problem ... that's the problem.

SCENE 3:

K. is in paramedic greens uniform.
He is sitting on an office chair, waiting.
There is a flipchart to his left.

I've made it to the training course, anyway. Me ... a paramedic, who would have thought it? I certainly never would have. I used to run a mile from any bodily fluids when I was younger, but you change though, don't you? I feel as though I've grown into myself. It's taken me long enough. Pushing 40 and still training. The thing is though, this time it's for a job I really want to do. I knew it had to be a big change. Well, there can't be many people who segway from wine grower to paramedic, but it feels right to me. I can come home after a shift and know that I've made a difference to someone's life. It's made a difference to my life too. A "win/win" I would have called it in a former existence.

It's not just the work either, it's the people you work with. As well as helping patients, they've helped me. It's amazing what close bonds you have when you're dealing with life and death situations or even just someone throwing up all over you. I've never known it before in my life. Someone counting on me to do the right thing to get them through the tough times. Beats the tedium of tying vines, any day.

I'm hoping Jenny will be on this course today. I think she will be, even though she's much more highly qualified than me. She's always been a paramedic. Always known what she wanted to do. I've never really known. I think she's got four kids, someone said. Imagine that, four kids! That would have been mine and Emily's worst nightmare. Still, Jenny looks well on it. Family life obviously suits her. She always seems 'up', always smiling. She's got a lovely smile. I see it quite a lot when we've been partnered up together on shifts so that I can learn from her, I've seen her smile change a frightened, elderly man into a real joker who is laughing along with us paramedics. Amazing. Anyway, I hope she's here today. Oh, here we go, the first lot are just turning up … better get my act together…

SCENE 4:

Night time.
K. is still in his paramedic greens.
He leans forward in an armchair.
He looks exhausted but pleased.

Blimey! What a night shift! Only just got through it. There's been all sorts kicking off tonight on Prince of Wales Road. Good job there are ambulances already in position, waiting to tend the fallen, by which I mean the ones who have actually fallen because they are smashed out of their minds or they've decided to scramble their brains with drugs. It makes me think of how it must have been on the battlefield, actually, one casualty after the next in a constant, desperate stream. I ended up answering the last call of the night, going out to a woman in a flat who hadn't been out of her front door for eight years. Jenny was with me on that call. It's a good job she was. The woman was morbidly obese, laid in bed, starting with sepsis and couldn't get out of the door. You can just picture the scene can't you? 'There's only one way we can get her out' Jenny said, 'It's going to have to be through the window. Can you ring for a cherry picker?' I panicked for about ten seconds, thinking that cherry pickers were only needed for building work, then realized here was the voice of experience talking and got straight onto headquarters to get the equipment we needed.

Jenny and I chatted while we waited for the cherry picker to arrive. Turns out she has four children but no man around. She seems to have had the knack of picking useless men or perhaps that's just me being biased. She seems even more of a wonder woman to me, now I know that. We got the fat lady out and into the ambulance after a lot of very inelegant manoeuvering by her, us and the cherry picker and as I drove the ambulance, I could hear Jenny in the back, cajoling this most grotesque, awkward woman into letting her take some observations. 'I wonder if this is how she cajoles her children' I thought to myself. 'With a smile like that, she could cajole me into doing anything.'

'You did well, tonight' she said as we finished cleaning the ambulance. 'You've got a real connection with people, which helps' she said. 'Really? Sometimes I don't seem to connect with people at all', I said. 'Well, you've connected with me' she said, and flashed her gorgeous smile again. 'Would you like to come round and meet the kids sometime?' 'Yeah, I'd love to meet your kids', I replied. Now there's another sentence I never thought I would hear myself say ...

SCENE 5:

K. is looking smart, in corduroys and a casual sweater.
He is pouring himself a whisky to take to bed
He is looking contented

I feel like having a drink, to celebrate. Whisky, not wine these days. Nothing in particular, but it's not often in your life that you feel that warm glow of contentment, that safe, secure certainty of knowing you've found the right person. You know that they're not perfect and you're not perfect but, somehow all the imperfections seem to fit together and not matter anymore. Tonight, being part of Jenny's family meal, listening to the kids tell her about the ups and downs in their day, betraying their lazy streaks, their stubbornness, their over-confidence, their generosity, their determination, their hopes and ambitions, the whole messiness of family life on show for me to see … . Well I loved it. It's something I've never had, never thought I wanted, never thought I needed until now. It's something real, isn't it, real life? Just like the job that Jenny and I do. Yes, it's messy but when did a bit of mess do anyone any harm? I knew I wanted to make a difference to people's lives when I changed jobs. What I hadn't bargained for was how much of a difference would happen to me … Cheers!

[Raises his whisky glass and smiles broadly].

ACKNOWLEDGEMENTS

I would like to thank my right hand woman, Marie for her invaluable skills which have seen me through this project and many others. I would also like to thank my friends, Celia and Angela who have provided endless encouragement and critical feedback. My great appreciation goes to the team at Matador who have been wonderful. Finally, I would like to express my heartfelt thanks to my husband, Nigel who has always believed in me.